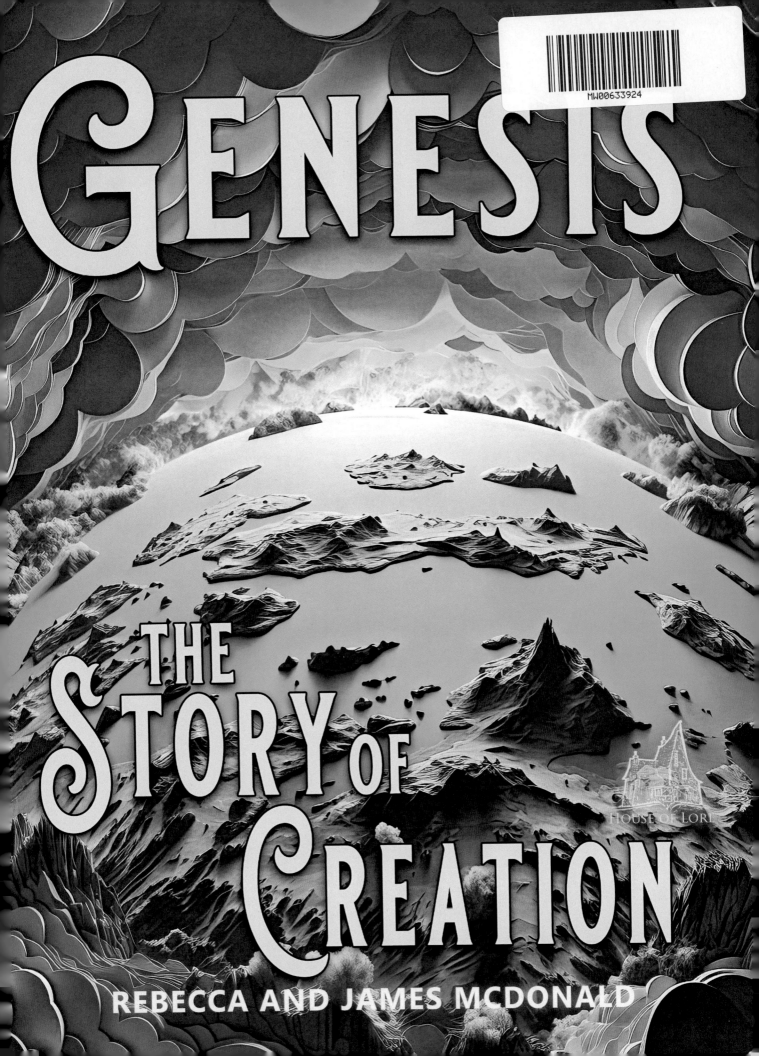

GENESIS

THE STORY OF CREATION

REBECCA AND JAMES MCDONALD

Let us pray.

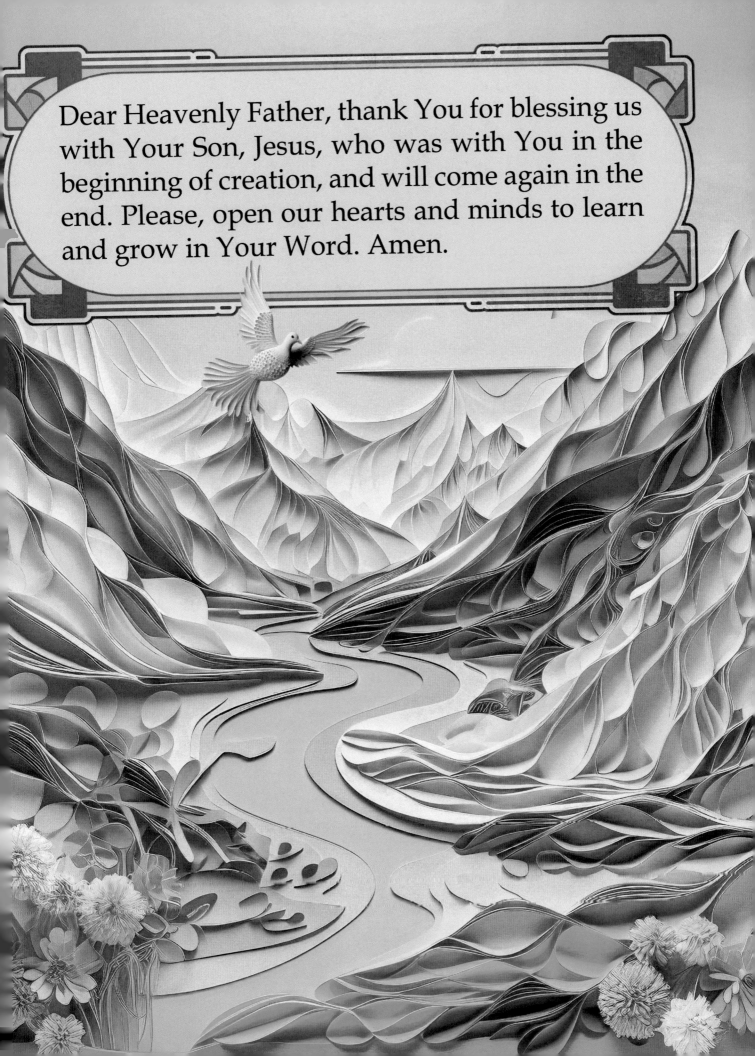

Dear Heavenly Father, thank You for blessing us with Your Son, Jesus, who was with You in the beginning of creation, and will come again in the end. Please, open our hearts and minds to learn and grow in Your Word. Amen.

The earth was dark and empty, but in the darkness, God's Spirit moved over the water.

On the first day of creation, God brought light to the darkness. "He called the light Day, and the darkness Night."

On the second day of creation, God divided the water above from the water below, and the space between these waters God called, Heaven.

On the third day of creation, God brought together the water so that the dry land appeared. He called the land, Earth and the gathered water He called, Seas.

Then God said, "Let the earth bring forth green herb," and plants began to grow and cover the land with colorful beauty.

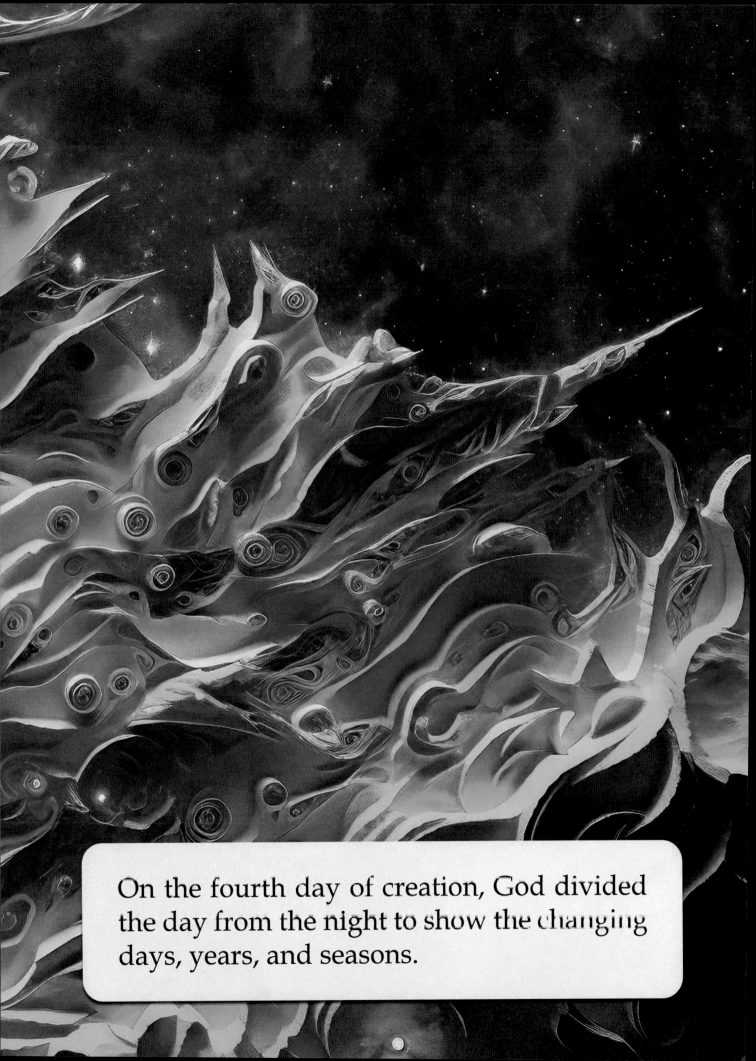

On the fourth day of creation, God divided the day from the night to show the changing days, years, and seasons.

God created the sun for bright days and the smaller moon to softly light the dark of night, and "God saw that this was good."

On the fifth day of creation, God created creatures to fill the seas and birds to fill the sky, adding birdsong and chatter to the sound of moving water.

God made giant whales and every type of fish to swim in the warm and cool water of the seas.

On the sixth day of creation, God created every kind of creature to live on the land, from the lowest valley to the highest mountain top.

God created man and woman, and
He made them in His own image.

God blessed man and woman so that they would increase and multiply and look after all of the creatures on the earth and in the seas.

And God saw that all He had made was good.

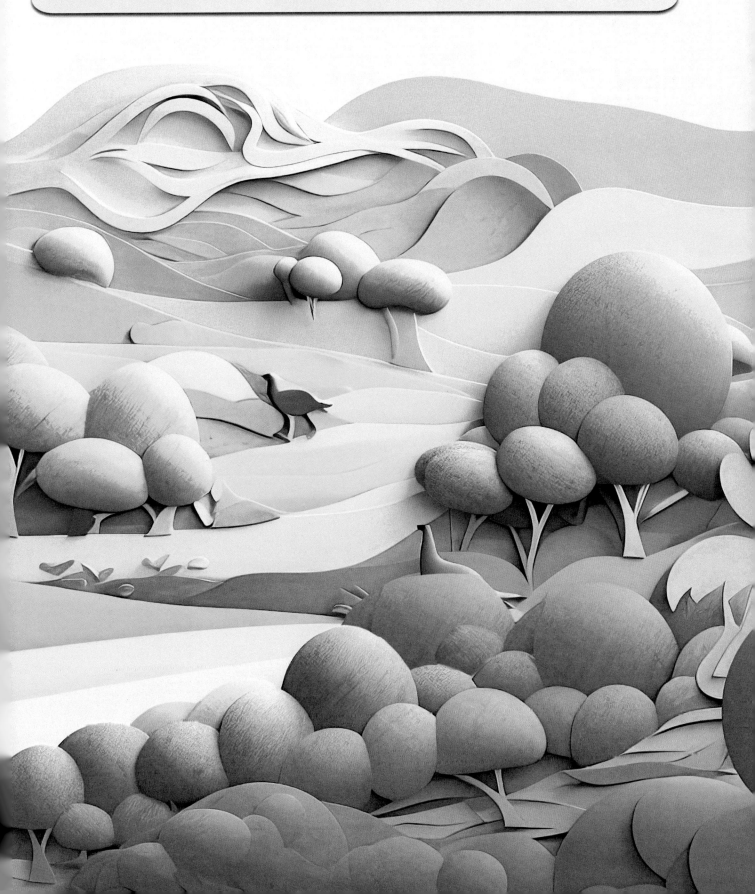

God blessed the seventh day and rested from all His work of creation.

These are the days of creation when God made heaven and earth, bringing light to the darkness and life to the emptiness.

Thank You Lord for blessing us with Your creation, and Your eternal Word, and let us always remember that all things are fulfilled in Your Son, Jesus Christ.

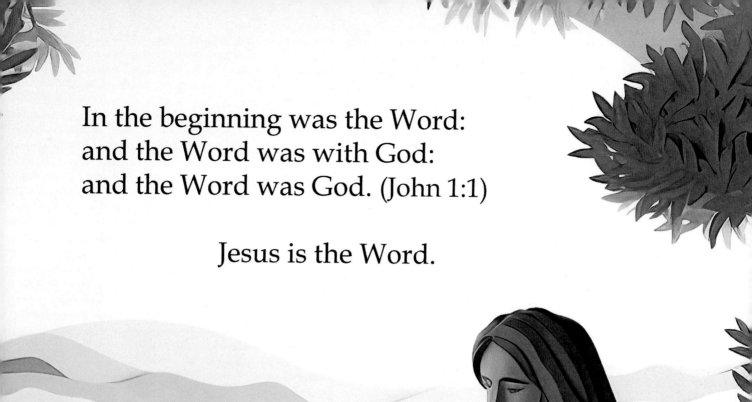

In the beginning was the Word:
and the Word was with God:
and the Word was God. (John 1:1)

Jesus is the Word.

QUESTIONS TO CONSIDER:

Who created all things?

What did God create in the beginning?

Why do you think God rested on the seventh day?

Who was with God in the beginning of creation?

Who will come again in the end?

Who is the Word?

Why is it important to pray?

Genesis, The Story of Creation

The Douay-Rheims version of the Holy Bible was used for all quotes, reference, and research for this book.

ISBN: 978-1-950553-35-8   First House of Lore paperback edition, 2023